The Super Sleuths have done it again!

WHO AM I?

Circle the correct answer.

Tigger   Darby

Eeyore   Roo

Rabbit   Pooh

Just because you are small doesn't mean...

...that you can't do big things.

Unscramble

Rabbit's favorite food.

srtcoar

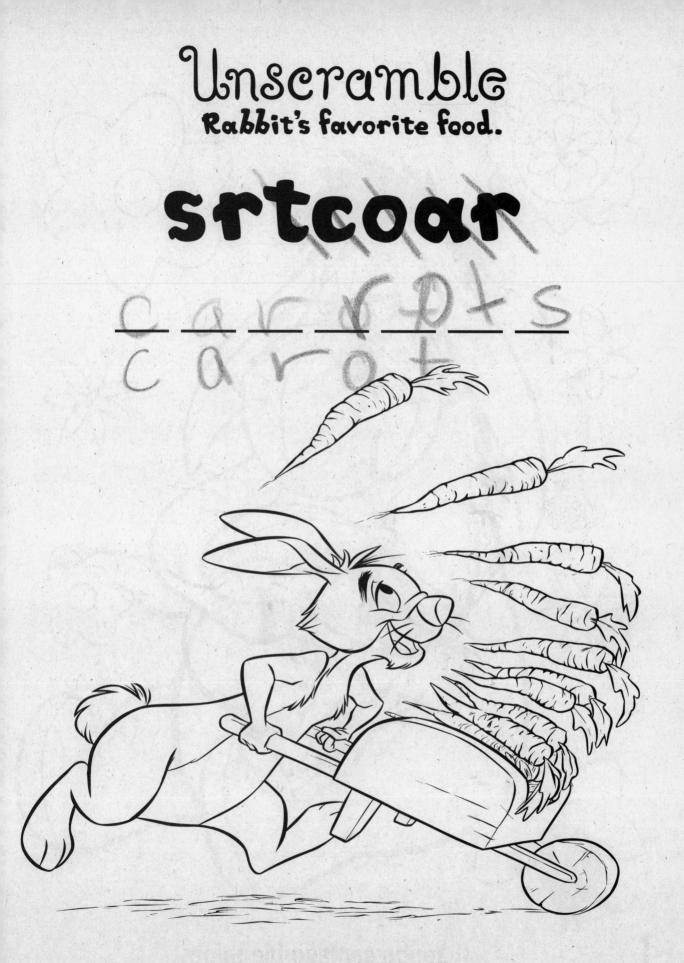

c a r r o t s

c a r o t

You're my favorite pal.

Follow the line
that leads from Lumpy to the bee.

A
B
C

your answer:

Connect the dots.

Find a clue like Pooh.

Color by Number

1 - yellow   4 - pink
2 - red   5 - green
3 - blue   6 - purple

Easy as peasy

Creative Edge

When the flag is high, it's time to fly.

Draw!
Piglet in the frame below.

100 acRe WooD

Maze Time!
Help Tigger find
the ladybug!

start

finish

Best Friends

Creative Edge

We're solverating a mystery!

Color by Number

1 - yellow
2 - red
3 - blue

Slap my cap!

You're my favorite pal.

PIGLeT

Hoo-hoo-ray!

Draw

Tigger in the frame below.

Creative Edge

☆ Hidden Pictures ☆
Circle the
🐝 hidden bumblebees. 🐝

Another mystery is history.

All suited up and ready for Super Sleuthing!

Easy as peasy.

CONNECT THE DOTS.

Creative Edge

Super Sleuth Scooters

Color by Number

1 - orange
2 - light pink
3 - dark pink
4 - green
5 - yellow

Which one is DIFFERENT?

A

B

C

D

your answer:

HOO-hoo-ray!

USE THE GRID TO DRAW POOH.

It's "I love you" day!

Eeyore

Creative Edge

Hello, Hundred Acre Wood Friends.

Look up, down, across and
diagonally for these words:

FRIENDS
HONEY
BEES
WOOZLE
BALLOON

Z Q T U F N U O B
B V F R I E N D S
R A H I V B W Y Z
A D L H Y V E U C
K W T L N N X E V
L T U G O M U V S
C W B H O O V Y R
W O O Z L E N Q F

RABBIT

Tigger-iffic!

CONNECT THE DOTS.

Whoooooooooooosh!

WHO AM I?

Circle the correct answer.

Piglet   Pooh

Tigger   Eeyore

Rabbit   Roo

Which line leads to Tigger?

A

B

C

your answer:

Answer: A

Lumpy the Heffalump

Use the grid to draw Piglet.

Look up, down, across and diagonally for these words:

POOH   RABBIT

PIGLET   DARBY

TIGGER   ROO

EEYORE   KANGA

```
Q  G  J  K  T  R  R  O  O
X  E  O  K  Y  F  N  V  W
B  L  E  B  A  T  P  J  R
S  M  R  Y  I  N  I  X  O
P  A  W  B  O  C  G  Z  W
D  O  B  N  T  R  L  A  L
Z  A  O  M  C  B  E  H  F
R  Y  U  H  K  L  T  D  T
G  T  I  G  G  E  R  C  P
```

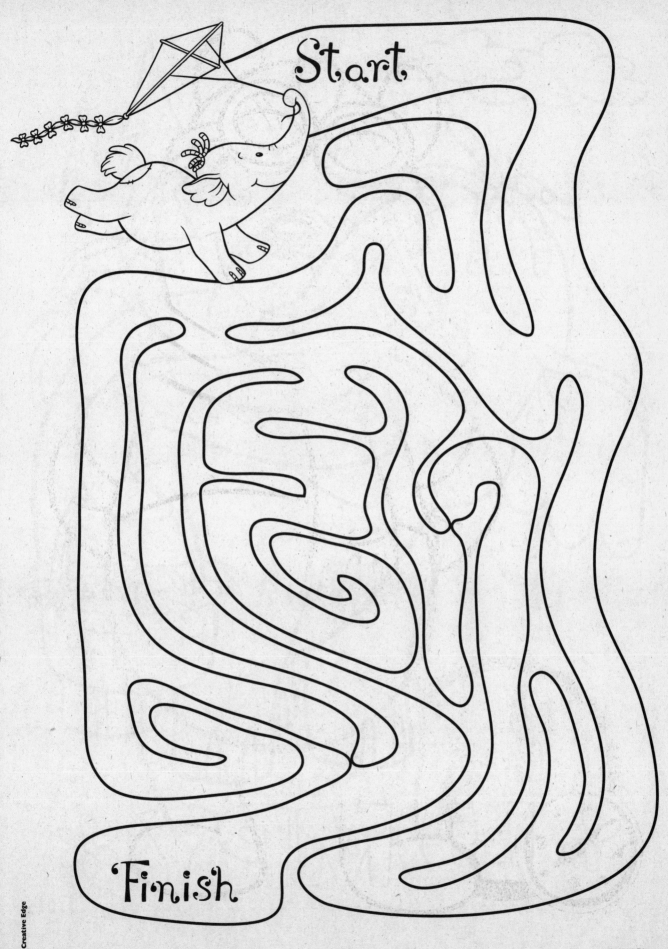

Start

Finish

LUMPY

Unscramble the names of these friends who live in the Hundred Acre Wood.

ORO

GRETGI

OHPO

BATIRB

NAKGA

Answers: Roo, Tigger, Pooh, Rabbit, Kanga

I L♥Ve YOU DAY

Which line leads to Eeyore?

your answer:

Unscramble
the word.
rfiedsn

___ ___ ___ ___ ___ ___ ___

How do I say I love Roo?

WHO AM I?

Circle the correct answer.

Pooh **Piglet**

Rabbit **Tigger**

Darby **Eeyore**

Answer: Piglet

Just because you're small...

...doesn't mean you can't do big things.

1. _____ the Pooh
2. Pooh's very good friend is _____.
3. Tigger loves to _____.

TIGGER

Darby and Buster

Which line leads to Pooh?

A

B

C

your answer:

Answer: B

Let's take a look and say I wonder,

think it over, think it under.

Which one is DIFFERENT?

your answer:

Answer: C

I LOVE You Day!

HUNNY

Kanga and **Roo**

CONNECT THE DOTS.

© 2007 Disney

Creative Edge

EEYORE

I'm Darby.

This is my pup, Buster.

I love you day!

LUMPY
HEFFALUMP

Use the grid to draw the flower.

INSTRUCTIONS

Tape or zigzag the edges of the Aida cloth to prevent fraying. Find the center of chart and center of fabric; begin stitching there.

Use two plies of floss or one strand of blending filament to work cross-stitches *except* blended needle; work blended needle as specified in key. Work backstitches using one ply of floss.

For beaded fringe on sleeves, thread a needle with two plies of floss. Knot the ends. Push the needle from the back of the fabric to the front at the first dot. Thread five seed beads onto the floss. Push needle back through the fabric near the dot. Pull snuggly to secure the bead loop. Repeat for all the dots.

To attach sequins to halo, use two plies of floss. Push the needle from the back of the Aida fabric to the front at the first dot, through the hole in the sequin, then through the bead, and back through the hole in the sequin and fabric. Pull floss snuggly. Repeat to attach sequins to halo at all dots.

Trim Aida fabric ½ inch beyond the top stitches of the halo and ¼ inch beyond the stitches at the sides and the bottom. Use the Aida cloth as a pattern to cut a back piece from the velvet. Using a ¼-inch seam allowance, sew the squares together along the bottom and the sides, right sides facing. Turn right side out and stuff with fiberfill.

Turn the raw edges of the fabric under ¼ inch along the top opening and tack one end of the ribbon in each top corner of the ornament. Sew the opening closed.

★★★HUG ME ANGEL

Finished ornament measures 4½x3½ inches.

MATERIALS
FABRICS
7x7-inch piece of 18-count white Aida cloth
6x5-inch piece of gold lamé fabric

THREADS
Cotton embroidery floss in colors listed in key on page 6
Rayon embroidery floss in color listed in key on page 6
Metallic cord in color listed in key on page 6

SUPPLIES
Needle; embroidery hoop
Gold petite seed beads (Mill Hill 40557)
Tracing paper
Two 3x4-inch pieces of light-weight cardboard
Crafts glue
Polyester fiberfill
⅜ yard of ¼-inch-diameter gold metallic twisted cord
¾ yard of ¼-inch-diameter ivory braid
3x3-inch piece of cardboard

INSTRUCTIONS

Tape or zigzag the edges of the Aida cloth to prevent fraying. Find the center of the chart and the center of the fabric; begin stitching there.

Use two plies of floss or one strand of cord to work cross-stitches. Work backstitches using one ply of floss or one strand of cord.

For necklace, thread needle with one strand of cord; knot end. Push needle from back of fabric to front at left side of angel's neck. Thread twenty-nine beads onto cord. Push needle back through fabric at right side of neck. Knot cord at the back of fabric.

Trace pattern, *page 6,* onto tracing paper; cut out. Use pattern to cut two ovals from light-weight cardboard. Center the stitchery atop one oval; trim ½ inch beyond edge of cardboard. Use Aida cloth as a pattern to cut one lamé oval. Center lamé on one cardboard oval; fold edges to back, clipping fabric as necessary to lie smooth; glue. Repeat with Aida cloth and remaining oval, leaving small area unglued near top; allow glue to dry. Stuff ornament front through opening with fiberfill; glue opening edges to back. Glue backs of oval together.

Cut gold twisted cord to fit around ornament and glue cord around edges of cardboard. Cut ivory braid into two pieces and glue one piece just inside cord on both front and back.

For tassel, cut a 4-inch and a 36-inch strand of gold cord; set aside. Wrap one strand *each* of Christmas red (DMC 321), pistachio (DMC 320), garnet (DMC 816), and forest green (DMC 986) floss and gold cord around 3x3-inch piece of cardboard several times. Thread 4-inch strand under wrapped thread at one edge of cardboard and tie. Cut thread at opposite edge of cardboard and remove. Wrap 36-inch strand of cord around thread bundle, ½ inch from top, and tie. Trim ends even; glue tassel to bottom of ornament.

For hanger, twist together one 6-inch-long strand each of Christmas red and forest green floss and two 6-inch strands of metallic cord thread; knot ends together. Tack knotted end to ornament top.

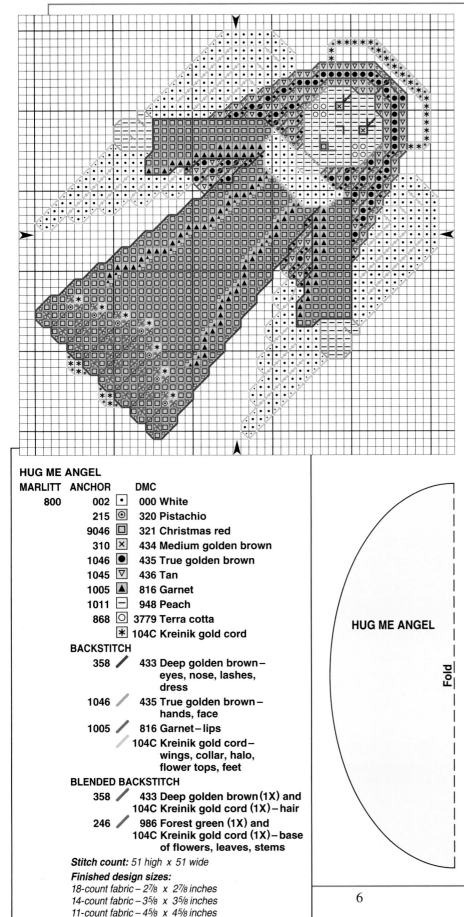

HUG ME ANGEL

MARLITT	ANCHOR		DMC
800	002	⊡	000 White
	215	⊙	320 Pistachio
	9046	☐	321 Christmas red
	310	☒	434 Medium golden brown
	1046	●	435 True golden brown
	1045	▽	436 Tan
	1005	▲	816 Garnet
	1011	⊟	948 Peach
	868	○	3779 Terra cotta
		✳	104C Kreinik gold cord

BACKSTITCH

358	╱	433 Deep golden brown – eyes, nose, lashes, dress
1046	╱	435 True golden brown – hands, face
1005	╱	816 Garnet – lips
	╱	104C Kreinik gold cord – wings, collar, halo, flower tops, feet

BLENDED BACKSTITCH

358	╱	433 Deep golden brown (1X) and 104C Kreinik gold cord (1X) – hair
246	╱	986 Forest green (1X) and 104C Kreinik gold cord (1X) – base of flowers, leaves, stems

Stitch count: 51 high x 51 wide

Finished design sizes:
18-count fabric – 2⅞ x 2⅞ inches
14-count fabric – 3⅝ x 3⅝ inches
11-count fabric – 4⅝ x 4⅝ inches

★★★SHIMMERING GLORY

Finished ornament is 4¼x3¾ inches.

MATERIALS

FABRICS
7x6-inch piece of 18-count white Astoria cloth
5x5-inch piece of blue-green fabric
Two 5x5-inch pieces of polyester fleece

THREADS
Cotton embroidery floss in colors listed in key
Blending filament in colors listed in key
Metallic embroidery thread in color listed in key

SUPPLIES
Needle
Embroidery hoop
Petite seed beads in color listed in key
Two 3-millimeter red rhinestones
Crafts glue
Four 1.5-millimeter red rhinestones
6-millimeter gold bead cap
Tracing paper
5x5-inch piece of heavy card stock
15 inches of ½-inch-wide antique gold metallic braid
2 yards of antique gold metallic thread or fine cord

INSTRUCTIONS
Tape or zigzag edges of fabric to prevent fraying. Find center of chart and center of fabric; begin stitching there.

Use one ply of floss, one strand of blending filament, or one strand of metallic thread to work cross-stitches unless otherwise specified. Work backstitches using one ply of floss

HUG ME ANGEL

Fold

SHIMMERING GLORY

or one strand of blending filament unless otherwise specified in key. Attach a seed bead at each dot in wings using one ply of blending filament.

Glue one large rhinestone to center of neck as indicated by large symbol. Glue smaller rhinestones as indicated by small symbols. Glue the remaining large rhinestone to the inside of the bead cap; glue the bead cap to the empty square at the waist.

Trace the pattern, *right,* onto tracing paper and cut out. Using the pattern, cut two arch shapes from the polyester fleece and one each from the card stock and the blue-green fabric. Center the tracing paper pattern on top of the stitchery, with the bottom edge of the

pattern ½ inch below the bottom row of stitches in the design. Draw around the pattern and cut out the stitchery.

Baste one piece of fleece to the back of the stitchery and the other to the back of the blue-green fabric, stitching close to the edges. Glue one fleece-backed piece to each side of the card stock. Fold the braid in half lengthwise and glue around the perimeter of the stitchery, covering the raw edges of the fabrics.

Cut the 2 yards of metallic thread or fine cord into six 12-inch-long strands. Align the strands and knot the ends together. Tack the knotted end to the top of the ornament. Remove any basting not covered by braid.

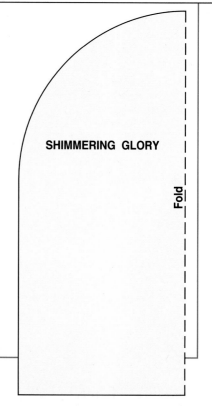

SHIMMERING GLORY

Fold

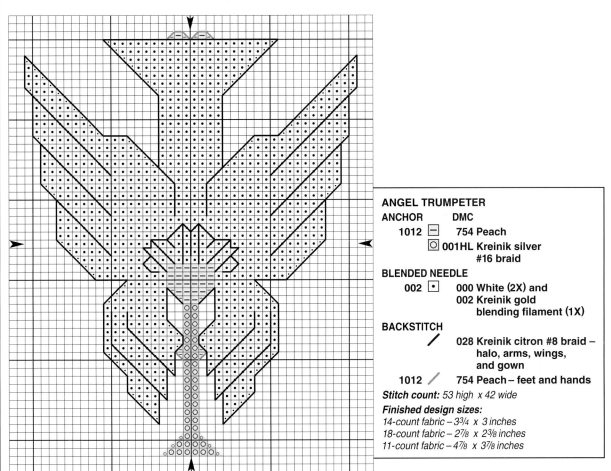

ANGEL TRUMPETER

ANCHOR		DMC	
1012	⊟	754	Peach
	◎	001HL	Kreinik silver #16 braid

BLENDED NEEDLE

| 002 | · | 000 White (2X) and |
| | | 002 Kreinik gold blending filament (1X) |

BACKSTITCH

| | / | 028 Kreinik citron #8 braid – halo, arms, wings, and gown |
| 1012 | / | 754 Peach – feet and hands |

Stitch count: 53 high x 42 wide

Finished design sizes:
14-count fabric – 3³⁄₄ x 3 inches
18-count fabric – 2⁷⁄₈ x 2³⁄₈ inches
11-count fabric – 4⁷⁄₈ x 3⁷⁄₈ inches

ANGEL TRUMPETER

★★ANGEL TRUMPETER

Finished ornament measures 3³⁄₄x3¹⁄₄ inches.

MATERIALS
FABRICS
5x5-inch piece of 14-count white Aida cloth
5x5-inch piece of white self-stick felt

THREADS
Cotton embroidery floss in colors listed in key

Blending filament in color listed in key
#8 braid in color listed in key
#16 braid in color listed in key

SUPPLIES
Needle; embroidery hoop

INSTRUCTIONS
Tape or zigzag the edges of the Aida cloth to prevent fraying. Find the center of the chart and the center of the fabric; begin stitching there.

Use two plies of floss or one strand of braid to work cross-stitches *except* blended needle;

work blended needle as specified in the key. Use one ply of floss or one strand of braid to work backstitches.

Remove the backing from the felt and center the sticky side on the back of the completed stitchery. Press to stick. Cut around the angel one square beyond the stitching.

For hanging loop, twist two 4-inch-long strands of #8 citron braid together and knot the ends together. Tack the knotted end of the loop to the ornament behind the angel's feet.

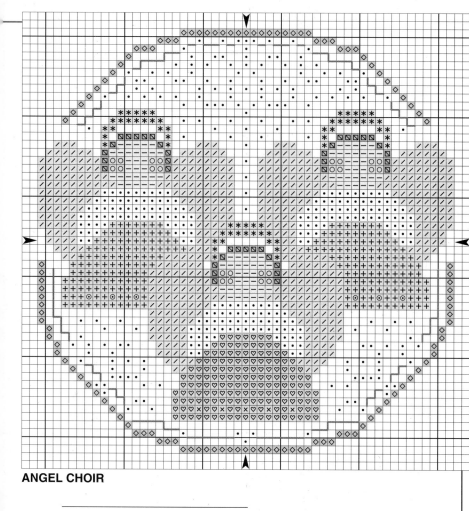

ANGEL CHOIR

ANGEL CHOIR

ANGEL CHOIR			
ANCHOR		DMC	
875	⊙	503	True blue green
1042	☒	504	Pale blue green
1012	◯	754	Medium peach
378	◩	841	True beige brown
1011	–	948	Light peach

BLENDED NEEDLE

002	·	000 White (1X) and 093 Kreinik star mauve blending filament (1X)
398	⁄	415 Pearl gray (1X) and 001 Kreinik silver blending filament (1X)
1012	♡	754 Medium peach (1X) and 093 Kreinik star mauve blending filament (1X)
886	✳	3047 Yellow beige (1X) and 002 Kreinik gold blending filament (1X)
049	⊞	3689 Mauve (1X) and 093 Kreinik star mauve blending filament (1X)
120	⊠	3747 Periwinkle (1X) and 093 Kreinik star mauve blending filament (1X)

BACKSTITCH

	⁄	002 Kreinik gold blending filament – skirt waist
049	⁄	3689 Mauve and 093 Kreinik star mauve blending filament– border

Stitch count: 53 high x 53 wide
Finished design sizes:
18-count fabric – 2⅞ x 2⅞ inches
14-count fabric – 3¾ x 3¾ inches
11-count fabric – 4⅞ x 4⅞ inches

★★ANGEL CHOIR

Finished ornament is 4 inches in diameter.

MATERIALS

FABRICS
5x5-inch piece of 18-count ivory Aida cloth
5x5-inch piece of pink taffeta fabric
Two 3½-inch-diameter circles of polyester fleece

THREADS
Cotton embroidery floss in colors listed in key
Blending filament in colors listed in key

SUPPLIES
Needle
Embroidery hoop
Two 3½-inch-diameter circles of medium-weight cardboard

Crafts glue
¼ yard of ¼-inch-wide ivory ribbon
⅜ yard of ¼-inch-diameter white twisted satin cord with pearls

INSTRUCTIONS

Tape or zigzag edges of Aida cloth to prevent fraying. Find center of chart and center of fabric; begin stitching there.

Use two plies of floss to work cross-stitches *except* blended needle; work blended needle as specified in key.

Work backstitches using one strand of blending filament or one ply of floss and one strand of blending filament.

Center stitched design atop one cardboard circle; trim excess fabric 1 inch beyond edge of cardboard. Use Aida cloth as a pattern to cut a circle from pink taffeta.

Glue one polyester fleece circle to one side of each cardboard circle. Center the stitchery over the padded side of one cardboard circle. Glue edges to back, clipping as necessary and pulling the fabric taut. Repeat with remaining cardboard circle and taffeta.

Fold ribbon in half, tack ends together. Glue ribbon ends to ornament top on back of one cardboard circle. Glue backs of circles together. Glue white cord around perimeter, covering the edges.

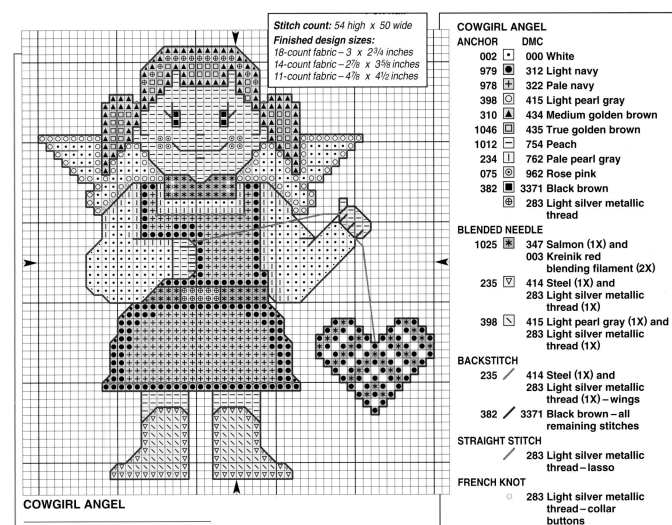

Stitch count: 54 high x 50 wide
Finished design sizes:
18-count fabric – 3 x 2¾ inches
14-count fabric – 2⅞ x 3⅝ inches
11-count fabric – 4⅞ x 4½ inches

COWGIRL ANGEL

ANCHOR		DMC	
002	·	000	White
979	●	312	Light navy
978	+	322	Pale navy
398	○	415	Light pearl gray
310	▲	434	Medium golden brown
1046	□	435	True golden brown
1012	–	754	Peach
234	I	762	Pale pearl gray
075	⊙	962	Rose pink
382	■	3371	Black brown
	⊕	283	Light silver metallic thread

BLENDED NEEDLE

1025	✳	347	Salmon (1X) and 003 Kreinik red blending filament (2X)
235	▽	414	Steel (1X) and 283 Light silver metallic thread (1X)
398	◺	415	Light pearl gray (1X) and 283 Light silver metallic thread (1X)

BACKSTITCH

235	/	414	Steel (1X) and 283 Light silver metallic thread (1X) – wings
382	/	3371	Black brown – all remaining stitches

STRAIGHT STITCH

	/	283	Light silver metallic thread – lasso

FRENCH KNOT

	○	283	Light silver metallic thread – collar buttons

SEED BEADS

	●		Red seed beads – 3 on skirt, 2 on collar, 1 on hair

COWGIRL ANGEL

★★COWGIRL ANGEL

Finished ornament measures 4⅛x4½ inches.

MATERIALS
FABRIC
Two 6x6-inch pieces of 18-count ivory Aida cloth
THREADS
Cotton embroidery floss in colors listed in key
Metallic embroidery thread in color listed in key
SUPPLIES
Needle; embroidery hoop
Red seed beads
Ivory sewing thread

INSTRUCTIONS
Tape or zigzag edges of one piece of Aida; set other piece aside. Find center of chart and center of prepared Aida cloth; begin stitching there.

Use two plies of floss or two strands of metallic thread to work cross-stitches *except* blended needle; work blended needle as specified in key. Work backstitches using one ply of floss unless otherwise specified in key. Use two strands of metallic thread to work French knots.

For beaded fringe on shirt, thread a needle with two plies of true Christmas red floss (DMC 666); knot ends. Push the needle from back of fabric to front at first dot. Thread two beads onto floss and push needle back through fabric near dot. Pull floss snug to secure bead loop. Repeat for all dots on shirt. Work fringe on skirt in same manner *except* use three beads at each dot.

For lasso, tie a knot about ½ inch from one end of a strand of metallic thread. Push the needle from the front of the fabric to the back at the base of the angel's right hand and back out at the top of the hand. Complete the lasso as shown on the chart; secure with a knot on the back.

Position completed stitchery on top of unstitched Aida cloth square, wrong sides together. Machine stitch pieces together, four rows beyond cross-stitches, on all sides. Fringe Aida cloth up to machine stitching. Trim fringe to ½ inch.

Fold a 6-inch strand of metallic thread in half and loop through top of ornament; knot ends of thread together.

CROSS-STITCH BASICS

GETTING STARTED

Cut the floss into 15- to 18-inch lengths and separate all six plies. Recombine the plies as indicated in the project instructions and thread into a blunt-tipped needle. Rely on the project instructions to find out where to begin stitching the piece.

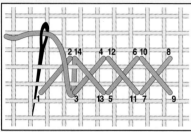

Basic Cross-Stitch in Rows

BASIC CROSS-STITCH

Make one cross-stitch for each symbol on the chart. For horizontal rows, stitch the first diagonal of each stitch in the row. Then, work back across the row, completing each stitch. On linen and evenweave fabrics, stitches are worked over two threads as shown in diagram, above. For Aida cloth, each stitch fills one square.

HOW TO SECURE THREAD

The most common way to secure the beginning tail of thread is to hold it under the first four or five stitches.

To finish, slip threaded needle under previously stitched threads on wrong side of fabric for four or five stitches, weaving thread back and forth a few times. Clip thread.

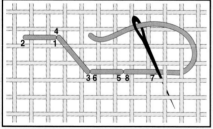

Backstitch

BACKSTITCHES

Backstitches are added to define and outline the shapes in a design. For most projects, backstitches require only one ply of floss. On color key, (2X) indicates two plies of floss, (3X) indicates three plies, etc.

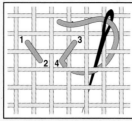

Quarter Cross-Stitch

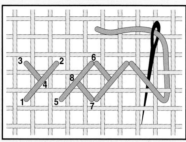

Three-Quarter Stitch

QUARTER AND THREE-QUARTER STITCHES

Quarter and three-quarter stitches are used to obtain rounded shapes in a design. On linen and evenweave fabrics, a quarter stitch extends from the corner to the center intersection of threads. To make quarter stitches on Aida cloth, you'll have to estimate the center of the square. Three-quarter stitches combine a quarter stitch with a half cross-stitch. Both stitches may slant in any direction.

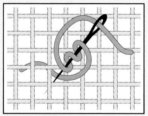

French Knot

FRENCH KNOT

Bring threaded needle through the fabric and wrap floss around needle as illustrated. Tighten the twists and insert needle back through same place in fabric. The floss will slide through the wrapped thread to make the knot.

CHART RATINGS

EASY	★
EXPERIENCED	★★
SKILLED	★★★
EXPERT	★★★★

★★★GLORIOUS ANGEL TREE TOPPER

Finished angel is 11 inches tall.

MATERIALS

FABRICS

Two 15x18-inch pieces of 28-count white Monaco fabric

Two 10x12-inch pieces of polyester fleece

THREADS

Cotton embroidery floss in colors listed in key on page 15

Metallic embroidery thread in colors listed in key on page 15

SUPPLIES

Needle

Embroidery hoop

Sewing thread

Gold metallic, red, blue, and black seed beads (optional)

1 yard of 1¼-inch-wide gold metallic flat lace

Erasable fabric marker

Two 9x12-inch pieces of clear plastic canvas

⅓ yard of ⅛-inch-diameter red and green cord

5-inch piece of ⅛-inch-wide blue satin ribbon

15-inch piece of ¼-inch-wide gold metallic ribbon

⅝-inch gold metallic cowbell

INSTRUCTIONS

Tape or zigzag the edges of the Monaco fabric to prevent fraying. Find the center of one piece of Monaco fabric and the center of the angel front chart; begin stitching there.

Use three plies of floss to work cross-stitches over two threads of the Monaco fabric. Work blended needle as specified in the key. Use one

ply of floss or one strand of metallic embroidery thread to work the backstitches.

Work the angel back chart in the same manner on the remaining piece of Monaco fabric. If desired, sew black beads to eyes, red beads to the scroll, blue beads to the dress front, and gold beads in a random pattern to the front and back of halo.

Press the finished pieces from the back. Baste fleece to the wrong side of each piece, stitching 1/8 inch beyond the edge of the cross-stitches.

Trim the sides and top of fabric 1/4 inch beyond the basting line. Trim the bottom edge 1/2 inch beyond cross-stitches. Sew lace to the angel front along the basting line.

Sew the front to back, right sides facing, along the basting line, leaving the bottom open. Clip the curves, turn right side out, and press.

Carefully trace the angel's outline onto one piece of plastic canvas with the marker. Cut out the canvas 1/8 inch inside of the marked outline. Use canvas as a pattern to cut the remaining piece of plastic canvas.

Roll one piece of the plastic canvas and insert it inside the angel, pushing it against the front of the angel. Repeat with the remaining piece of plastic canvas, pushing this piece against the back.

Turn the bottom edge of the fabric up over the bottom of the plastic canvas. Hand-stitch the cord to the bottom fold of the fabric.

Tie blue satin ribbon into a bow and tack it to angel front under the scroll. Sew cowbell to the center of angel's waist on back. Tie the gold ribbon into a bow and tack above the cowbell. Trim ribbon ends.

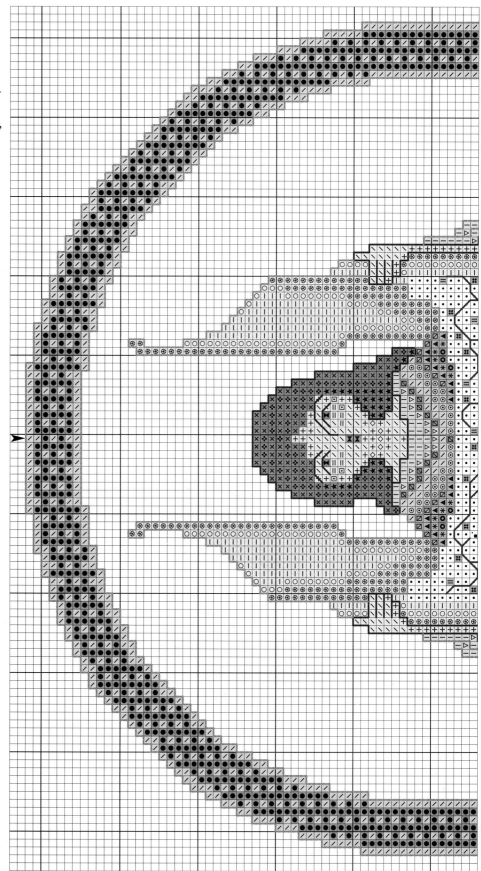

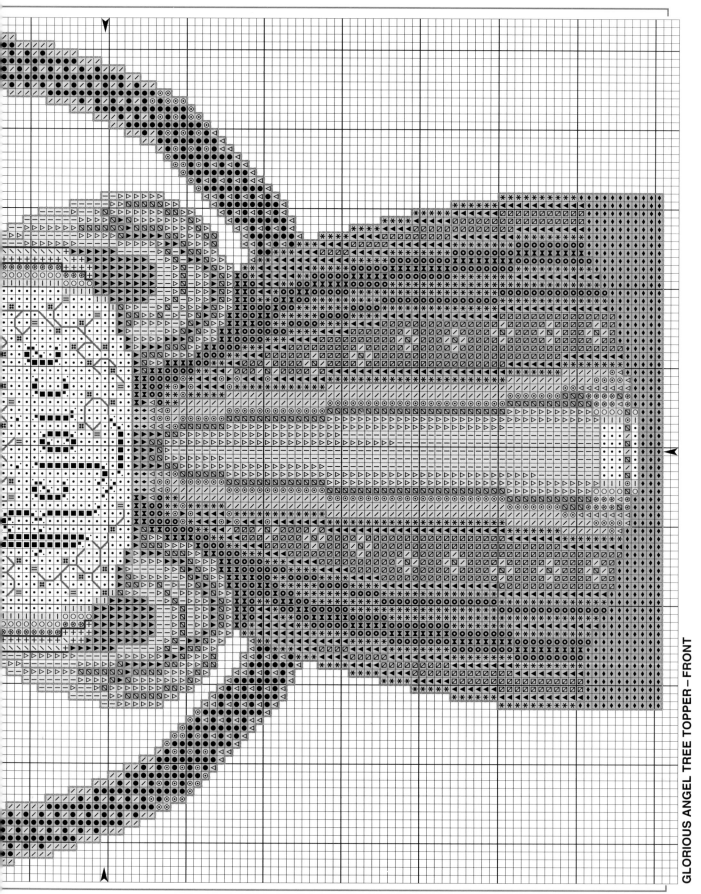

GLORIOUS ANGEL TREE TOPPER – FRONT

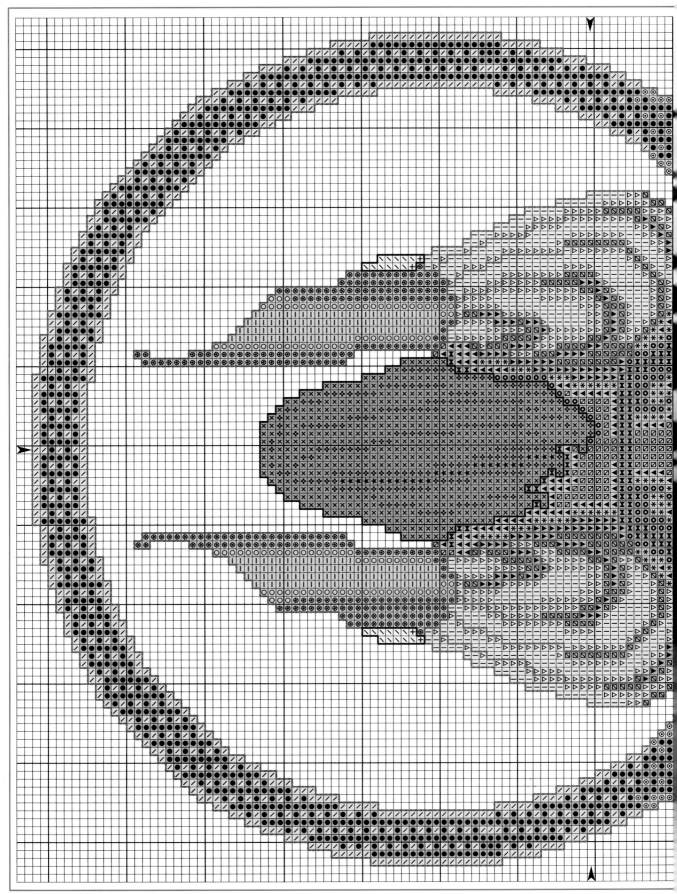

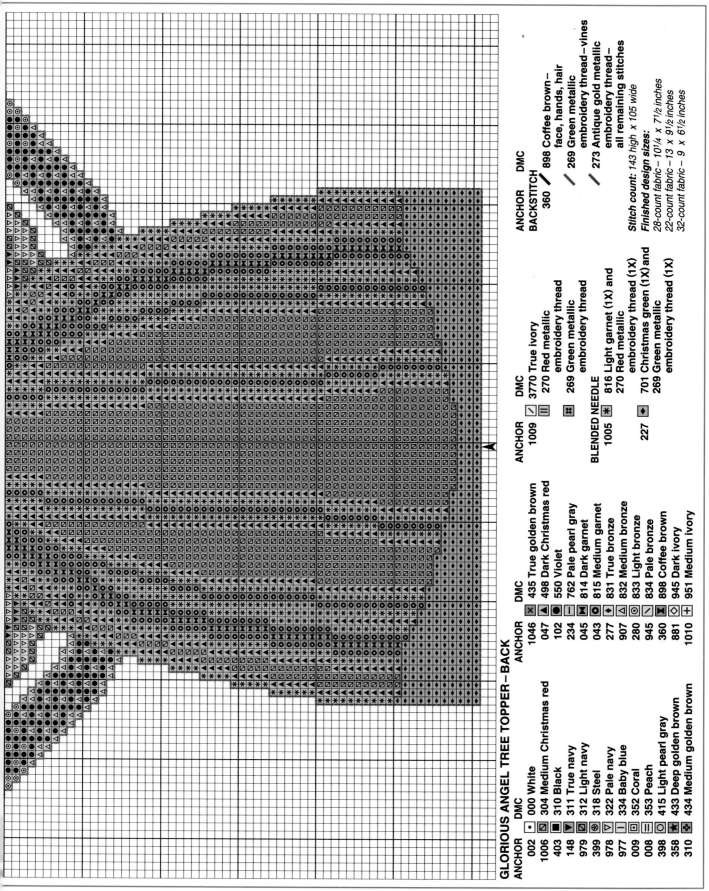

GLORIOUS ANGEL TREE TOPPER–BACK

ANCHOR		DMC
002	•	000 White
1006	▨	304 Medium Christmas red
403	■	310 Black
148	▶	311 True navy
979	▨	312 Light navy
399	✦	318 Steel
978	▷	322 Pale navy
977	—	334 Baby blue
009	⊡	352 Coral
008	꞊	353 Peach
398	◯	415 Light pearl gray
358	★	433 Deep golden brown
310	✚	434 Medium golden brown
1046	✕	435 True golden brown
047	◀	498 Dark Christmas red
102	●	550 Violet
234	∣	762 Pale pearl gray
045	✕	814 Dark garnet
043	◉	815 Medium garnet
277	◆	831 True bronze
907	◁	832 Medium bronze
280	◎	833 Light bronze
945	╱	834 Pale bronze
360	▣	898 Coffee brown
881	◇	945 Dark ivory
1010	➕	951 Medium ivory

ANCHOR		DMC
1009	▱	3770 True ivory
	▥	270 Red metallic embroidery thread
	✚	269 Green metallic embroidery thread

BLENDED NEEDLE

ANCHOR		DMC
1005	✳	816 Light garnet (1X) and 270 Red metallic embroidery thread (1X)
227	◆	701 Christmas green (1X) and 269 Green metallic embroidery thread (1X)

ANCHOR		DMC
BACKSTITCH
360	╱	898 Coffee brown– face, hands, hair
	╱	269 Green metallic embroidery thread–vines
	╱	273 Antique gold metallic embroidery thread– all remaining stitches

Stitch count: 143 high x 105 wide

Finished design sizes:
28-count fabric – 10¼ x 7½ inches
22-count fabric – 13 x 9½ inches
32-count fabric – 9 x 6½ inches

15

Glorious Angel Tree Topper

What could be more beautiful than a heavenly cross-stitched angel adorning the top of a sparkling holiday tree? Our lovely cherub is accented with metallic threads and glistening beads and was designed especially to coordinate with our prizewinning angel ornaments. Complete instructions and charts begin on page 11.

PHOTOGRAPHER: SCOTT LITTLE

EAN

UPC

$4.95 Price higher in Canada